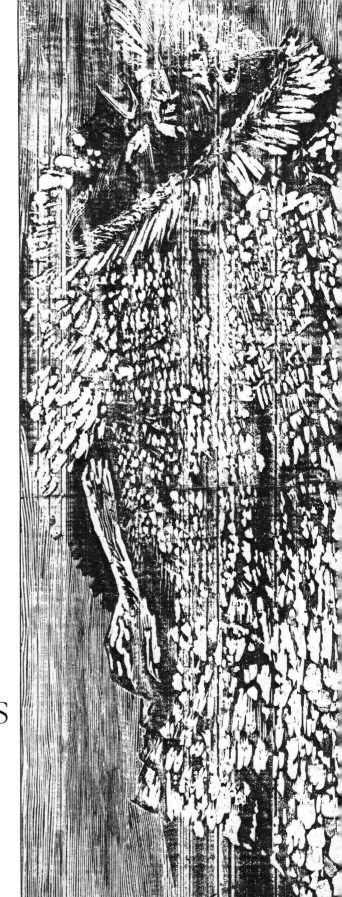

MAORI LEGENDS

The Return of Ruru

MAORI LEGENDS

illustrated by
Roger Hart

with text by
A.W. Reed

A. H. & A. W. REED WELLINGTON/SYDNEY/LONDON

First published 1972
Reprinted 1973, 1976, 1978

A.H. & A.W. Reed Ltd
65-67 Taranaki Street, Wellington
53 Myoora Road, Terrey Hills, Sydney 2084
11 Southampton Row, London WC1B 5HA
also
16-18 Beresford Street, Auckland
Cnr Mowbray & Thackeray Streets,
Waltham, Christchurch 2

ISBN 0 589 00707 6

Typesetting by Consolidated Press Holdings Ltd.
Wellington.
Printed by Kyodo Printing Co. Ltd., Tokyo

CONTENTS

COLOUR PLATES

INTRODUCTION

THE GODS OF AOTEAROA are found in many islands of Polynesia, but in no other place were the cosmogony and pantheon of gods more clearly and imaginatively defined than among the Maori people, who lived close to nature and endued their surroundings with unending variety of personifications of natural phenomena — personifications that were the descendants of the departmental gods who controlled earth, sea, and sky.

The Maori peopled his world, the Ao-marama, or "World of Light", with such gods and manifestations. He had his own vivid account of the creation of the world, the separation of earth and sky, the clothing of the Earth Mother, and the ornamenting of the Sky Father with sun, moon, and stars by Tane-matua. Tangaroa, the god of the sea, is ever at war with Tane of the forests, and both are attacked by Tawhiri-matea, the god of winds. Rongo, the god of peace and cultivated lands, stands in strong contrast with Tu-matauenga, the god of war. The humble fern root, so tasteless yet often so necessary to survival, had its own departmental deity in the form of Haumia-tiketike.

The cycle of legends centred on the cult hero Maui outrivalled those of the same demi-god who was well known throughout the Pacific basin.

Although scholars now regard the later revelations of Whatoro and Te Matoro-hanga with some suspicion, there is reason to believe that the Maori had set foot on what Elsdon Best described as "the long road that leads to monotheism". Nevertheless, to all except the most learned tohunga the adventures of the gods had an important influence on thought and custom, and provided assurance that man and his surroundings were under the guardianship of supernatural forces that were prepared to protect those who honoured them.

In more homely mood there were tender stories of love and endurance, tales of monsters and ghostly creatures of the night and the mist-enshrouded forests, together with firm belief in an after-life. There were many atua, deities to be appealed to in time of war or crisis, and enchanted logs and stones that possessed magical qualities. The inner recesses of the forest were peopled with fairy-like folk, supernatural animals preyed on humans, and malignant sea creatures invaded the land by night.

Natural phenomena were explained by tales of ingenious invention. There were many stories of the sun, moon and stars. Mountains, rivers and lakes were given names and characters and frequently acted as human beings, as also did the trees and forest plants, the wind and the weather.

There were fearsome revelations of the evil powers of wizards, tales of flying men, giants, witches and wild men of the forest. In the field of human activity there were stories of cultivation and home-making, voyages and journeys on sea and land, the playing of games, fishing, hunting, and waging of relentless wars.

Matau and Matakauri

From this rich treasure-store Roger Hart has selected subjects to illustrate varied aspects of Maori lore. It is a peculiarly personal representation, for every artist must add something of himself to his work; but he has also succeeded in capturing something of the very spirit of Maori belief in the supernatural. He takes us behind the scenes, as it were, so that we walk with him in the realms of natural and supernatural life that are a thousand years away from the sophisticated, material universe with which we are so familiar.

In compiling the text, the author has adapted many of the legends from his earlier, comprehensive volume *Treasury of Maori Folklore*, and to a lesser extent the more popular *Myths and Legends of Maoriland*.

A. W. REED.

MYTHS, LEGENDS AND FOLK TALES seem always to spring from and retain the characteristics of the landscapes of their origins. So, the Black Forests of Germany automatically conjure up the images of the Brothers Grimm; the soft twilights of Scotland evoke Celtic folklore and the tales of Bonnie Prince Charlie; the harsh expanses of Australia give immediate meaning to the Aboriginal stories of earth, fire and water.

Thus the New Zealand landscape, different from these, lends its own characteristics to the legends of the Maori; stories of trees, mountains, lakes, demons, fairies, underwords and overworlds, and all manner of phenomena that affected his daily existence.

It is from this viewpoint that I have illustrated this book—the figures are to be seen as being part of the landscape, whatever it is that may be happening to them. The landscapes are mostly real, be they with or without figures, and represent places which are, for me, very strong in their evocations of legendary and supernatural occurrences.

Such is Lake Waikaremoana, which forms the background to several of the illustrations. When the mists descend, and all is grey and still, the concept of *patupaiarehe* and *taniwha,* ogresses and giant birds become more than real; one becomes aware of pervasive forces very different from those of the Pakeha, and no doubt only fully understood by the Maori. However, it is this world, through the medium of paint and ink that I have, perhaps foolishly, tried to enter.

ROGER HART

CREATION

Listen to the chants of creation

Lift, lift up the south land.
Upward, upward lift the south sky.
Put each in its own position
There to rest for ever.
Lift, lift up Rangi,
And with offering made to thee, O Rangi,
We lift thee up!

Stand apart the skin,
Be divided the skin,
As the nettle to the skin,
As the tataramoa to the skin.
Do not grieve for your partner,
Do not cry for your husband.
Let the ocean be broken,
Let the ocean be far apart;
Be you united to the sea,
Yes, to the sea, O earth;
Broken asunder are you two.
Do not grieve,
Do not continue your love,
Do not grieve for your partner.

IN THE BEGINNING WAS Te Kore, the Nothing, and from Te Kore came Te Po, the Night. In that impenetrable darkness Rangi the Sky Father lay in the arms of Papa the Earth Mother.

Then gods, who were their children, crawled through the narrow space between their clinging bodies. They longed for freedom, for wind blowing over sharp hill tops and deep valleys, and light to warm their pale bodies.

"What can we do?" they asked. "We need room to stretch our cramped limbs. We need light. We need space."

The Tane-mahuta, mighty father of the forest, father of all living things that love light and freedom, rose to his feet. For as long as a man can hold his breath Tane stood, silent and unmoving, summoning all his strength. He pressed his hands against the body of his mother and planted his feet firmly on his father. He straightened his back and pushed against the Sky Father.

The primal parents clung to each other. Tane exerted all his strength, straining back and limbs, until at last the mighty bodies of earth and sky were forced apart.

"It was the fierce thrusting of Tane that tore the heaven from the earth," was an ancient saying of the Maori people. "So they were sent apart, and darkness was made manifest, and so was the light."

Rangi was hurled far away while angry winds screamed through the space between earth and sky.

Tane and his brothers looked at the soft curves of their mother. As the light crept across the land they saw a veil of silver mist that hung over her naked shoulders—the mist of grief for her lost husband. Tears dropped fast from Rangi's eyes. The showers of rain ran together in pools and streams across the body of the Earth Mother.

Although he had separated his parents so forcibly, Tane loved them both. He set to work to clothe his mother in beauty that had not been dreamed of in the dark world. He brought his own children, the trees, and set them in the earth. But Tane was like a child learning by trial and error the wisdom that had not yet been born. He planted the trees upside down. Their heads were buried in the soil, while the bare white roots remained stiff and unmoving in the breeze.

It was no place for his other children, the birds and the insects. He pulled up a giant kauri, shook the soil from the branches, set the roots firmly in the ground, and proudly surveyed the spreading crown set above the clean, straight trunk. The breeze played with the leaves, singing the song of a new world.

The earth lay still and beautiful, wrapped in a cloak of living green. The ocean lapped her body, the birds and the insects ran and fluttered in the fresh breeze. The brown-skinned gods frolicked under the leaves of the garden of Tane. Each had a duty to perform. Rongo-ma-tane preserved the fertility of the growing things of earth. Haumia-tiketike tended the humble fernroot. Tu-matauenga was the god of war. Tangaroa controlled the restless waves. Only one of the seventy brothers left the placid shelter of his

The Separation of Rangi the Sky Father and Papa the Earth Mother

mother to follow his father. It was Tawhiri-matea, the god of all the winds that blow between earth and sky.

Tane-mahuta raised his eyes to where Rangi lay, cold and grey and unlovely in the vast spaces above the earth and was sorry for the desolation of his father. He took the bright sun and placed it on Rangi's back with the silver moon in front. He travelled through the ten heavens until he found a garment of glowing red. After that he rested for seven days, and then spread the cloak across the sky from east to west and north to south.

But Tane was not satisfied. He decided that the gift was not worthy of his father and stripped it off. A small piece remained, a fragment of the garment men still see at the time of the setting sun.

"Great father," Tane cried, "in the long dark nights before Marama the moon shines on your breast, all things sorrow. I will journey to the very ends of space to find adornment for you."

Somewhere in the silence he heard an answering sigh. He passed swiftly to the very end of the world, into the darkness, until he reached Maunganui, the Great Mountain, where the Shining Ones lived. They were the children of Uru. The two brothers watched them playing at the foot of the mountain.

Tane begged Uru to give him some of the Shining Lights to fasten on the mantle of the sky. Uru rose to his feet and gave a great shout. The Shining Ones heard and came rolling up the slope to their father. Uru placed a basket in front of Tane. He plunged his arms into the glowing mass of lights and piled the Shining Ones into the basket.

Tane placed five glowing lights in the shape of a cross on the breast of Rangi and sprinkled the dark blue robe with the Children of Light. The basket he hung in the wide heavens. It is the basket of the Milky Way. Sometimes Uru's children tumble and fall swiftly towards the earth, but for the most part they remain like fireflies on the mantle of the night sky.

ADVENTURES IN THE UNDERWORLD

THE WINDSWEPT BEACHES of Northland are crowded with the hurrying footsteps of the souls of men. When the spirits of the dead reach the Reinga, where the ancient pohutukawa overhangs the Leaping Place of Spirits, they drop through the surging bull-kelp and find themselves in the underworld that men know as Rarohenga.

Little is known of that mysterious abode to which all men must go. There are strange tales of men and women who returned, but their accounts have little in common. Of these, the legend of Hine-marama, her husband Rangi-rua, and his brother Kaeo, is perhaps the most unusual.

Hine-marama died and her spirit went to the land of shadows. The heart-broken Rangi-rua enlisted the aid of his brother. Together they swung from the branches of the pohutukawa tree into the swirling waters that guard the entrance to Rarohenga. Emerging on dry land they followed the course of an underground stream until they saw a canoe coming to meet them from the far side. The evil-looking ferryman urged them to hurry, but the brothers were afraid to enter his frail canoe lest it should sink under the weight of their mortal bodies. Kaeo solved the problem by swimming across the river.

It was not long before Rangi-rua found his wife and clasped her spirit to him. She looked at him sadly. "I cannot come with you," she replied to his urgent plea. "You are man and I am spirit. You must return quickly. Do not eat the food of this place or you will never be released."

"Have you eaten of it?" asked Rangi-rua.

"Not yet, my husband. There has not been time, for I have scarcely arrived. But see! The hangi is steaming and the food will soon be ready. Take Kaeo with you and lose no time in returning to the Ao-marama."

"You have not eaten!" Rangi-rua shouted. "Then we can save you!"

The brothers caught her hands and ran swiftly to the bank of the river. Husband and wife jumped into the canoe while Kaeo swam by their side.

"The woman stays here," the ferryman said curtly. "You are a man. You have no place here, Rangi. Go quickly while I return this woman to her proper place."

He caught her by the hand but Rangi-rua pulled her away and threw her on to the bank. Kaeo placed his foot against the prow of the canoe and sent it surging back into the stream.

On reaching her home the spirit of Hine said, "You must wash my body. Then I can return to it and be your wife again in this world of light."

And so it was. By the bravery of Rangi-rua and his brother Kaeo, Hine-marama was snatched from the clutches of Hine-nui-o-te-po, the goddess of death.

Rangi-rua forces the Ferryman of Rarohenga to return
his wife to the World of Light

MAUI THE SUN-TAMER

Maui-nukurau—The Deceiver
Maui-whare-kino—The Evil House
Maui-tinihanga—The Many Devices
Maui-i-toa—The Brave
Maui-i-atamai—The Kind
Maui-mohio—The Wise
Maui-mata-waru—The Eight Eyes, The Supernatural.

These were some of the descriptive names applied to the whimsical, irresponsible demi-god of Polynesia. After a miraculous birth and upbringing he won the affection of his parents, taught useful arts to mankind, snared the sun, tamed fire, discovered new lands by pulling them up from the bed of the sea, and eventually met his death while attempting to kill the goddess of death, Hine-nui-o-te-po. His greatest deeds were of untold benefit to mankind, but his malicious humour made his relatives highly suspicious of his motives.

A persistent tradition, the only one that attempts to describe his appearance, says that one eye was like an eel, the other like pounamu, but it is difficult to imagine such a merry demi-god in so grotesque a mould.

Te Ra, the sun, travelled swiftly across the sky. The hours of daylight were short. The nights were long and there was barely time to cook the morning and evening meal, no time to cultivate the plantation, to make war, to hunt, to fish, no time even to love.

"I'm going to capture the sun and force him to move more slowly!" Maui said to his brothers.

"Why?"

"It will make the days longer."

"Listen," they said earnestly, knowing how much trouble some of his experiments had caused. "No good can come of such foolishness. Leave the sun alone."

Maui laughed. "We shall do it together."

"We can never tame the sun," they protested. "He would burn us up before we could get near him."

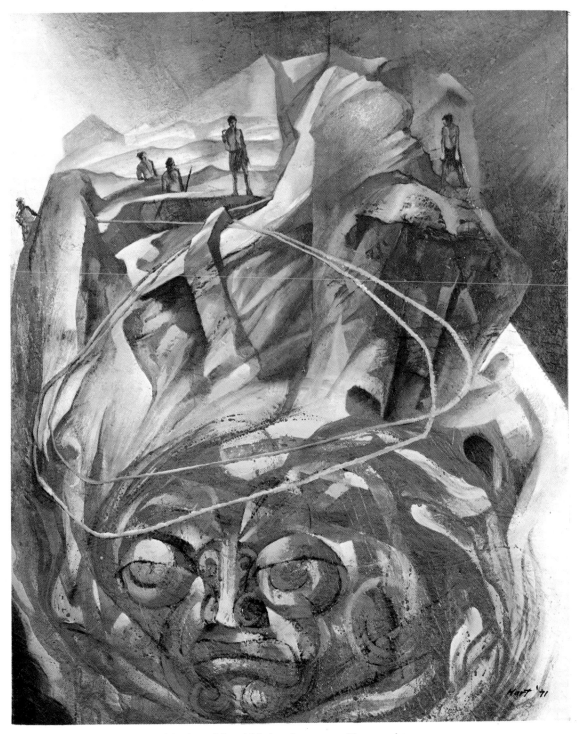

Maui-potiki and his brothers snare Tama-nui-te-ra

"Not if you follow my plan," Maui said eagerly. "We'll plait strong ropes of flax. Early tomorrow morning we'll take them to where the sun rises. We can easily build shelters to shield us from the heat."

After some persuasion his brothers reluctantly set to work to plait ropes for flax fibre. As it was an unknown art, Maui had to teach them how to spin the fibre into flat, round, and square ropes with three and five strands.

It was a long journey, but at last they reached Te Rua-o-te-Ra, the Cave of the Sun. When he rose above the horizon a coil of rope fell over his head and shoulders, and another and another.

"Pull hard," Maui shouted. "Don't let him get away."

Leaving his brothers to maintain the strain on the ropes, he ran towards the sun. From his girdle he pulled out his favourite weapon, the jawbone of his ancestor Muri-ranga-whenua, and belaboured the helpless sun until he cried for mercy. Maui chanted a powerful spell, known as a punga, to keep the sun from moving.

"Are you trying to kill Tama-nui-te-ra, the great son of the sun?" said Tama in a weak voice, as he struggled to break the ropes. It was a significant remark, for it was the first time that the sacred name of the sun had ever been revealed.

"I have no wish to harm you. If you promise to travel more slowly in future, I'll let you go."

"No," said great Tama stubbornly. "Why should I change my habits on your account?"

"This is why," Maui said and battered the sun until he was weakened. When he was released he limped so slowly across the sky that men and women were able to cook their food, eat, work, play and make love at their leisure, while from his wounds came the bright rays we know as sunbeams.

After his long labour and the heat of the sun, Maui was thirsty. He called Tieke, the saddleback, to bring him a drink of water. The bird took no notice. Maui caught it in his hands and hurled it into the water. Where his hot hands touched Tieke's back the feathers were burned brown. He called Hihi, the stitchbird, but it also ignored the demi-god. Maui threw it into a fire that tinged its plumage with yellow. Ever afterwards the stitchbird was nervous and timid. Toutouwai, the robin, was equally unco-operative and was marked with a patch of white at the root of its bill " as a mark of incivility". It was Kokako, the blue-wattled crow, who helped him. It flew to the water and brought back as much as it could carry in its ears. Maui rewarded it by pulling its legs so they were long and could move quickly.

There is another legend about Maui and the sun that refers to a period of perpetual daylight. The demi-god had become angered by the foolishness of mankind. They were so stupid that Maui felt the sunshine was being wasted on them. He held up his hand to stop the sunlight. It seems that he was unaware of the heat of the sun, for his hand was badly burnt. He rushed to the sea to assuage the pain and for the first time the sun set and darkness rushed across the land.

Maui rushed after the fleeing sun and dragged it back. It escaped and fled to the west. Maui pulled it back a second time and tied a long rope to it, attaching the other end to the moon.

When the sun set the moon was dragged above the horizon, giving light to the world by night as the sun had done by day.

Maui experimented more cautiously this time and found that he could hide the moon behind his hand without burning himself. Since then he has continued to use his hand to control the appearances of the moon.

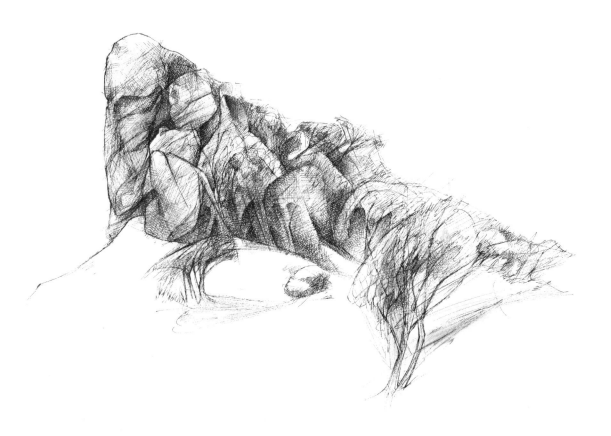

PATUPAIAREHE

Come back to O-te-patatu,
To the lofty dwelling
Where the sweet sounds are heard,
The sound of the fairy flute,
The music of the mountains
That thrilled me through and through.

THE MAORI had an implicit belief in the existence of patupaiarehe—a term which is usually translated "fairies". The use of the word can be misleading if we think of fairies as diminutive and lovable "little people", but is a proper expression in the sense of "imaginary supernatural beings or spirits, supposed to assume human form whether male or female, and to meddle for good or ill in the affairs of mankind".

To the Maori people of long ago they were real, dangerous to mortals, and large and white-skinned. They were found in several parts of the North Island, but were most numerous in certain localities such as Ngongotaha, Pirongia, and Moehau, where they were supposed to inhabit large fortified villages on the cloudy summits of the mountains.

The best known of the fairy legends comes from the experiences of Ihenga, the great explorer and name-giver of the thermal region. In the course of his journeys he came to Rotorua—Roto-rua-a-Ihenga, the second lake of Ihenga. Travelling around the shore, he reached the stream and mountain later known as Ngongotaha.

Ihenga was curious to know whether the plume that drifted lazily from the hilltop was smoke or mist. He climbed the slopes, undaunted by the plaintive songs he heard in the forest. From the corner of his eye he saw strange forms, and movements that showed he was being followed.

A breath of wind tore the mist away from the peak, revealing the palisades of a pa and a tree blazing like a torch. He broke off a branch that was alive with flame. Pale forms rushed towards him. Ihenga swung the crackling branch in a fiery circle that caused the patupaiarehe to retreat. He plunged it into the bracken, filling the air with choking smoke and stinging sparks and fled back to his canoe.

Some time later he settled by the Waiteti Stream and tried to establish relations with the elusive white-skinned people whose music echoed eerily through the mist. One day he climbed up to the hilltop pa and called to the red-haired people of the mist. They ran towards him. He asked for water and a beautiful young woman offered him a drink from a calabash with a wooden mouthpiece. Ihenga drank deeply while the patupaiarehe crowded around and commented on his appearance. Ihenga named the mountain from this incident. Ngongo means "to drink" and is also the word for the mouthpiece of a taha, or calabash.

Ihenga and the Patupaiarehe

The strange inhabitants of Te Tuahu-a-te-atua, the sacred place of the god, plied him with questions and touched his body with ghostly fingers. Ihenga grew afraid. He slipped through the palisades and hurtled down the hillside.

The patupaiarehe streamed after him. Gradually he drew away from the shouting throng, but one of the fairy creatures kept close on his heels. It was the young woman who had offered him her calabash. She threw her garments away to leave her limbs unhampered. Ihenga knew that if she captured him she would rob him of his memory, and he would never see his wife again.

In the pocket of his belt there was a small fragment of kokowai mixed with shark oil. Without faltering in his headlong flight he drew it out and smeared it over his body, for he remembered that the patupaiarehe were repelled by kokowai and that the smell of food and oil was repugnant to them.

With a cry that had sadness and longing in it as well as frustration, the comely girl from the fairy pa stood still. Ihenga looked back and saw her motionless amongst the trees with arms stretched out in mute appeal to the mortal man who had escaped her clutches.

The experience of Ruru, the husband of Tangi-roa, was more painful. While on a tuna-catching expedition, the young man was lost in the hills. Presently he stumbled into a clearing, and was immediately surrounded by white, ghostly forms that caught him and carried him away to their pa. For

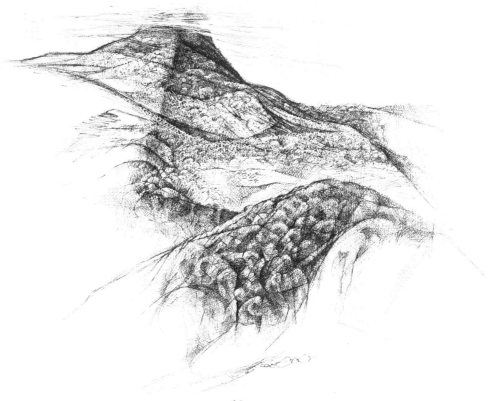

a long time he was kept in the strange comatose state of most captives of the patupaiarehe.

Attractive young women were usually loved and cared for by the male fairies, but Ruru was subjected to many indignities. They rubbed him with the palms of their hands and the soles of their feet until a moss or lichen grew from his skin and covered his body. The hair on his head fell out and he became completely bald.

After a time he was granted partial liberty. He was allowed to roam through the forest to search for berries and hunt for eels and birds; but as the patupaiarehe were unable to use fire in their damp retreat, the food was unpalatable.

Thinking that Ruru was dead, the aged tohunga Maringi-rangi sought to marry Tangi-roa, but was supplanted by a younger rival. The tohunga went to the seashore and wove spells of peculiar intensity, after which he lay down to sleep. When he woke he found a stranger sitting beside him. Maringi-rangi looked at him closely. The man was naked and covered with a peculiar moss-like growth in which the bald crown of his head lay like a polished boulder. The tohunga looked at him closely for a long time and then said, "You are Ruru! It is because of my magic that you have escaped from the patupaiarehe. Come with me."

He led Ruru along the beach and through the gates of the kainga. A cry of horror rose from the women, who shouted, "A madman!"

"Don't be afraid," Maringi-rangi said. "This is our old companion Ruru. Call Tangi-roa. Tell her that her husband has come to claim her once again as his wife."

Tangi-roa ran towards them, but recoiled when she saw the bald-pated, lichen-covered travesty of a man. Maringi-rangi led Ruru up to her and said with an evil smile, "Here is your reward, Tangi-roa. Welcome your lover and husband." The woman buried her face in her hands and wept bitterly. Looking down at her, the old tohunga's heart was touched. He remembered the passions and sorrows of his youth.

"Bring warm water quickly," he ordered.

Dipping his hands in the calabash, he repeated spells and incantations and rubbed the body of Ruru as the patupaiarehe had done when they had captured the young man. The kohukohu, or moss, came away freely and Ruru was restored to his wife—but to his dying day his skull remained as smooth as a water-worn boulder in the stream where he had hunted for tuna before he was caught by the fairy folk of the hills.

NOTE: The painting of Ruru and the tohunga appears as a frontispiece to this volume.

PONATURI

THE PONATURI were closely related to the patupaiarehe. They shared their aversion to the sunshine and strong daylight, but were creatures of the sea who came ashore only at night. One of the best known Maori legends is the account of how the cult hero Rata rescued his father's bones from the ponaturi. In the following tale Kaumariki lost his friends and barely escaped with his life from these repellent creatures of the sea.

The bone fish-hook named Te Rama possessed the property of attracting fish from a great distance. It was coveted by Kaumariki who dared to violate its tapu. With the help of two friends, Tawhai and Kupe, he stole the sacred fish-hook. Fearing the owner's revenge, they set sail in a canoe and did not stop until they reached a lonely island far across the sea. The water near the shore was teeming with fish.

"Look!" Kaumariki shouted. "Te Rama is already at work. The fish are leaping towards it."

They decided to wait until the following day. Kaumariki collected a heap of driftwood, but Tawhai and Kupe decided to keep out the cold of the night by heaping sun-warmed sand over their bodies.

"The sand will grow cold long before dawn," Kaumariki warned. "A hot fire is the only way to drive out the demons of cold."

He dragged the firewood into a circle, set it alight and lay down in the centre.

He was awakened by cries of terror. Looking across the dull embers of his fire he saw his friends imprisoned in their bed of sand fighting vainly against a horde of weird creatures. Their skins were a greenish white that glowed with putrescent light. Their fingers terminated in long claws with which they were tearing the skin from the helpless men.

Kaumariki piled dry wood on the fire, driving back the bolder ones who were advancing towards him. As soon as the flames died down the creatures rushed to attack him, retreating only as the frantic man fed the flames.

At daybreak the sea creatures disappeared into the sea. Kaumariki stepped cautiously over the charred timbers and went to the trenches where the bodies had been lying. There was no trace of his friends. Skin, flesh, blood,

Kaumariki, Tawhai, Kupe and Ponaturi

bones and hair had all been devoured. Kaumariki dared not face another night alone on the haunted island. He dragged the canoe into the water and headed for home.

On arrival at the pa he gave Te Rama back to its owner and admitted his offence. In view of what he had suffered, his theft was pardoned.

"I must avenge the death of my friends," he said. "Who will come with me? I need at least a hundred warriors and one of our largest war canoes."

"How can you ever overcome the ponaturi?" he was asked. "The bravest fighter is no match for the endless multitudes of the sea devils."

"If you do as I tell you we shall overcome them," Kaumariki replied. "Let the women collect raupo leaves and manuka stakes. We shall use them to build a whare on the island. While they are doing this you must cut down many trees and fashion the trunks into the shape of men."

Kaumariki took four gourds. He packed them with fungus and filled them with shark oil, intending to use them as lamps. When they were finished he wrapped them in bark covers.

The next day the heavily laden crew set off on its journey of revenge. As soon as it reached the island, everyone helped to unload the canoe and build a large whare-puni. When it was completed the wooden effigies, wrapped in cloaks, were placed on the floor.

The shadows deepened. Kaumariki posted a warrior in each corner of the building with a lighted lamp in his hands. The bark covers shielded the flame. In the subdued light it seemed as though many men were sleeping on the floor of the whare.

The remaining warriors sheltered inside a circle of fire that had been lit nearby. The hours passed slowly but everyone remained silent and alert. Towards midnight a whisper passed through the ranks of warriors. A dark shadow had appeared out of the water.

As it advanced up the beach the greenish-white skins of the ponaturi reflected the flames of the watchfire. It was joined by three more figures. The four ponaturi scouts, keeping well away from the fire, approached the whare. They peered through the open doorway, saw the motionless forms lying on the sandy floor and whispered, "Kei te moe! All are asleep." Their leader turned and repeated loudly, "Kei te moe!"

Hundreds of ponaturi rushed up the beach, struggled through the doorway and fell on the cloaked forms. When they were all inside Kaumariki gave a shout. The four warriors who had been standing motionless in the corners of the whare pulled the shades from their lamps. The ponaturi were blinded by the light. Holding their hands over their eyes, they rushed blindly to and fro, searching for the door. In the confusion the four warriors slipped outside.

Kaumariki barred the door and signalled to the warriors to apply torches to the brushwood walls. A few terrified sea creatures managed to escape through the blazing walls. The rest were burned to death in a blaze of light and burning heat as the flames soared upwards, transforming the whare into a fiery revenge for the death of Tawhai and Kupe.

OGRESSES

IN ADDITION to patupaiarehe and ponaturi the legendary world of the Maori was peopled with a number of different kinds of supernatural creatures—tipua or goblins, maero or wild men of the forests, and ogresses. Tales of Maori ogresses or witches were told in the whare tapere at night, to the huge enjoyment of the listener—though small children may well have clung to their mothers while the fitful flames caused dark shadows to pounce on the cowering tamariki.

Te Ruahine-mata-maori was unlike other ogresses who were notable for their repulsive appearance, for she was "the old woman with the face of a Maori".

The chief Paowa was a famous traveller and explorer. On one of his voyages he landed on a distant shore and was greeted by Te Ruahine, who invited him to partake of a meal. She took a basket of kumara from her stone pit and placed them in the earth oven. While they were cooking Paowa asked for a drink of water. In spite of her attractive appearance the chief recognised that she was an ogress and determined to outwit her. When she left her whare, he bewitched the spring, causing it to dry up. She went to a pool of water, but found only dry, cracked mud. Wherever she went the usual sources of water appeared to be exhausted.

Te Ruahine realised that Paowa had seen through her pretence of hospitality and understood that she intended to harm him. Looking back at her house she saw a column of smoke rising into the air. There was no sign of Paowa or his canoe.

She sat down and sang mournfully:

> *Let my house be burnt,*
> *But let my store remain.*
> *Let my house of enchantment be burnt,*
> *But let my fences remain.*
> *Let my filth-pot be burnt,*
> *But let my dogs remain.*

The ogress called her dogs and asked them where her visitor had gone. They followed the man-scent down to the waters, sniffed among the seaweed, and pointed their noses towards the horizon. Te Ruahine was satisfied. She placed some kura under her armpits, threw off her cloak, and waded into the sea. The power of the sacred red ochre enabled her to swim under water with incredible speed. After travelling in this manner for several kilometres, she came up to the surface and looked around. There was the canoe and, close at hand, the shore of a strange land. She submerged quietly and came up close to the canoe. Paowa had been keeping a careful watch while his men were paddling the canoe. When he saw her head and shoulders rising above the waves he urged the crew to paddle quickly to the shore.

The canoe bounded forward, but Te Ruahine-mata-maori drove onward with the speed of a waka taua, the water surging against her breasts, her legs threshing like the flukes of a sperm whale. She stretched out her hand to grasp the topstrake of the canoe. Paowa shouted a last command to his men to turn the canoe and paddle for their lives. As it left he jumped overboard and swam swiftly to the shore.

Paowa ran up the beach and took refuge in a cave, frantically piling boulders across the entrance while the ogress crossed the sand. By the time she reached the cave the barricade was firmly in position. She scratched at it vainly and then sat down in front of it.

Inside the cave Paowa busied himself kindling a flame with his fire drill. When the flames took hold of the dried grass and seaweed he added sticks of driftwood and roasted food on the hot stones. When it was ready he called· to Te Ruahine, "Old woman, where are you?"

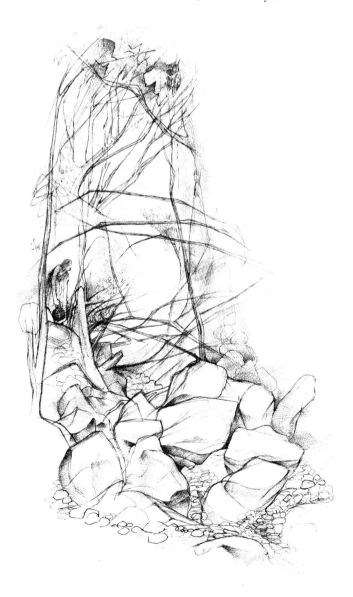

Te Ruahine-mata-maori and Paowa

"I am here, Paowa, waiting for you. You can't escape."

"I don't want to escape," he replied. "See, I've cooked some food for you. Now you can share a meal with me."

He pushed a few morsels between the stones. She snatched them and stuffed them into her mouth.

"Well, my mokopuna, that was a nice morsel, but I expect a proper meal from you."

"Don't be so impatient," Paowa said, "There's plenty left. Shut your eyes and open your mouth wide."

When her eyes were closed, Paowa broke down the barrier at the mouth of the cave and threw a red hot boulder into her cavernous mouth. Te Ruahine swallowed it and fell to the ground. Paowa came warily out of the cave and bent over her. The dreaded ogress was dead. He touched her and lightning flashed from her armpits.

"Aha! The Kura!" Paowa exclaimed.

He scooped it out and crawled into a hollow log lying close by. Then, by the power of the sacred kura, the log slid down the beach and propelled itself to his distant home, where his men received him as one returned from the dead.

GIANTS

THE ORIGINAL NAME of Lake Wakatipu in Central Otago was Whakatipua—the hollow of the giant. "Whaka" is a South Island variant of "Whanga", a harbour or hollow.

The tipua was a giant named Matau, who stole the beautiful girl Manata from her father's home on the plains. Her lover, Matakauri, set out in search of her and found her seated by the bank of a river.

"I have come to take you home," he said as he clasped her in his arms.

"Alas, my lover, I can never escape. Matau has tied me to him with a cord made from the skin of his two-headed dogs. It can never be broken."

Matakauri smiled confidently. He began to saw the cord with his maipi but the knife made no impression on the tough hide. Manata bent over it and, as her tears dropped on the leather thong, it dissolved and she was free. Holding hands, the lovers floated downstream until they reached the girl's home.

Knowing that his bride would never be safe from the giant, Matakauri determined to kill him. He waited until the northwest wind blew across the mountains and then set out on his quest. He soon found the place where Matau was sleeping soundly on a bed of bracken in the vast bowl of the hills. Creeping quietly round the giant he set fire to the dry fern. Fanned by the wind, the flames licked Matau's sides causing him to draw up his legs. Before he could regain consciousness he was suffocated in the dense smoke.

The flames were fed by the running fat. His body sank deep into the earth until it formed a vast chasm many kilometres in length and several hundred metres in depth. The whole body was consumed and reduced to ashes—all except the heart, which continued to beat strongly in its narrow tomb.

The wind died. The rain fell in torrents, pouring into the newly made gulf from many streams. The heat of the fire had melted the snow on the mountains, which fed the swiftly flowing rivers that poured into the Whaka of Matau. It was filled to the brim and remained a lake that has retained for all time the shape of the giant who drew up his knees when he felt the fierce heat of the burning bracken.

His heart still beats far below the surface of the water—sometimes fiercely, so that the lake is tormented by waves that beat angrily against the shore. More often the surface is placid as the water slowly rises and ebbs to the gentle heart beat of Matau the tipua. That is the story of the mysterious rise and fall of Lake Wakatipu—a phenomenon for which the Pakeha has no convincing explanation.

Legends of men of great stature vary from enormous beings like Matau to men like Tuhourangi who was six feet to his armpits and nine feet to the top of his head. When he shouted to his slaves from the shore of Rotorua he could be heard six kilometres away on the island of Mokoia. Tuhourangi was out-matched by Te Pute of Nga-puhi, whose eyes were as big as saucers, and whose sneeze could be heard from Punakitere to Kaikohe, a distance of nearly ten kilometres.

Toangina was another of giant stature. He was the scourge of the lower reaches of the Waikato river. When a canoe came in sight he swung himself from the bank on a long vine, plucked a victim from the canoe and killed him with a single blow from his fist. In this way he had slain the well-known chief Korongoi, cut up his body, and displayed the dismembered limbs as a warning to others.

Korongoi's son Te Horeta, though normally a brave warrior, was too faint-hearted to face up to Toangina until, at the incessant urging of his wife, he assembled a party of fighting men. They attacked the giant in his home until he was forced to flee. Te Horeta was in the vanguard of the pursuers. The giant turned at bay and in the conflict, the young chief's taiaha was broken. The jagged end pierced the puku of Toangina and so ended his reign of terror.

NOTE: The painting of Matau and Matakauri appears on page 7.

GIANT BIRDS

Aotearoa was the home of that great bird the moa, which, within the memory of the Maori people, roamed the plains and was hunted for food until it was exterminated; but for some unknown reason the fabulous birds of the land were always provided with wings.

The poua-kai may well have been the extinct eagle of the South Island. It lived on the summit of Tawera (Mount Torlesse) and preyed on the people of the plains. From its eyrie the man-eating bird maintained a constant look-out. As soon as it saw a party of travellers it spread its wings, swooped down, and carried them away to its nest, where it devoured them at leisure.

Ruru, a noted bird-hunter, was chosen to lead an expedition against the man-eating bird. There are several versions of the strategies he employed to snare it. In one of the more plainly embroidered accounts he chose fifty men to assist him. At Ruru's direction they cut a large quantity of manuka poles and carried them to a pool at the foot of the mountain. The poles were laced together to form a net over the water. The warriors crouched beneath it. Ruru lured the poua-kai to the wooden net and its legs were entangled in the poles. The men who were hidden underneath dragged them down and killed the helpless bird with their weapons.

In an even simpler form of the legend the poua-kai attacked a red-haired man, but its claws became entangled in his rough flax cape. The bird was unable to defend itself and was beaten to death by a band of warriors who had been lying in wait.

Some significance was attached to the fact that the object of the bird's attack was a red-head, and a saying was later applied to anyone with red hair: "Ha! The decoy of poua-kai!"

One of the best-known bird legends was that of a flying moa which conveyed Pou-rangahua, a man of great mana, from Hawaiki to Aotearoa. The chief had gone to the homeland to obtain kumara for his young son. On his return he was conveyed on the back of the bird and so established this important food crop in New Zealand.

Ruru and the Poua-kai

TANIWHA

The monster there!
Vast as a rock he lies!
How angrily his eyeballs glare!
How flash his fiery eyes!
Come Sleep, come Sleep;
Let the slumbrous spells be laid
In the depths below, in the depths below;
Let sleep be as of night,
Like the Great Night,
The Long Night,
The Sleep-bringing Night,
Sleep on—sleep on!

It is remarkable that there was such widespread belief in the frightening monsters known as taniwha in a land where there was no native creature that could give rise to such a concept. The crocodile-like shape of the taniwha has led to speculation that the imaginary monsters of Aotearoa may be a racial memory from tropical lands. The taniwha frequently resembled lizards, of which the Maori had a superstitious fear, believing them to be the visible representation of the powers that caused sickness and death.

Some specimens were believed to be harmless except when tormented or neglected. The ocean-dwelling taniwha were known to have escorted canoes and to have carried men on their backs; but generally speaking they were dangerous to mankind. Taniwha had a distinguished ancestry, having descended from the great atua Tane, who mated with Hine-tupari-maunga. Their daughter was married to Tane's brother and the fruit of their union was Tua-rangaranga, the direct progenitor of taniwha.

The Maori recognised the affinity of lizards and taniwha by giving them the same name, moko. The monsters usually frequented deep pools or lurked in dark caves, but there were several notable occasions when monstrous taniwha engaged in the earth-moving business, making considerable changes in the landscape.

There were three noted taniwha in the thermal regions—Hotu-puku, Peke-haua, and Kata-ore. It is of Hotu-puku that the following tale is told.

Many travellers between Rotorua and Taupo had failed to reach their destination. It was suspected that they had been ambushed by some hostile tribe. A taua was sent out to find the enemy and destroy them. As the party travelled across the plain the scent of the men crept into the nostrils of Hotu-puku who was lurking in a nearby cave.

The monster sprang out and rushed towards the unsuspecting men. The spines and excrescences on its back had the appearance of the growths on some fabulous creature of the sea. Some of the men were trampled to death,

Hotu-puku, the taniwha of the Kaingaroa plain

34

others were seized in the cavernous mouth and swallowed whole. Those who escaped stumbled into the pa at Rotorua and told the tale of their misadventures.

Another war party was quickly assembled and took the trail to Hotu-puku's lair.

On the way they discussed their plan of campaign. On arrival at Kapenga, where the taniwha still lurked, they stripped leaves from ti-palms and plaited them into strong ropes.

They waited until the wind blew away from the cave and climbed down to it. They could hear the monster's stertorous breathing. It was sleeping soundly. The rope snares were arranged at some distance from the cave while the men drew close to the entrance. They were armed with cutting and thrusting weapons. Others held the ropes while a third party, composed of the youngest and boldest of the warriors, stood at the mouth of the cave to lure the taniwha into the open. They advanced cautiously as the ground shook and the huge form of Hotu-puku filled the dark mouth of the cave. It came forward at a run, its jaws distended, its long tongue darting from side to side. As the taniwha rushed out, the warriors retreated. Their ropes were lying on the ground, seemingly scattered at random, but in fact they had been placed with great care. The men took care not to disturb them.

A sudden shout startled the taniwha. The noose sprang from the ground as a score of hands tugged at the ropes. Hotu-puku's front legs were caught in a crushing grip. Like living things the other ropes circled its legs and body. They wove themselves round its neck and jaws, falling lightly and then biting into the scaly flesh. Only the tail was free. It lashed from side to side, sweeping men off their feet as the monster felt the bite of mere and taiaha, and the sting of cutting implements.

Maddened with pain, Hotu-puku strained against the ropes as the nooses were pulled tighter. The ropes were wound round the trunks of trees, pegging the taniwha down firmly until it lay lifeless on the ground.

Its appearance was that of a huhu grub, if one can imagine such an object swollen to the size of a young whale, or of a tuatete, the now extinct "frightful lizard", with scales and spiny ridges.

One of the chiefs suggested that they throw off their garments and cut the monster open to inspect the contents of its belly. There were many layers of fat to penetrate, but once these were stripped off the excited warriors exposed a grisly treasure trove. There were bodies of men and women who had recently been eaten and were still undigested. There were many greenstone mere, thrusting weapons such as kokiri and taiaha, weapons made from the bone of whales, sharks' teeth, mats, garments of dogs' hair, cloaks ornamented with albatross, kiwi, and kaka feathers, garments of dressed and undressed flax, and precious heirlooms.

The human remains were interred, after which the taniwha was dismembered and oil expressed from its fat. It was eaten by the warriors to express their contempt and to celebrate victory over the enemy that had killed so many of their friends from Rotorua and Taupo-moana.

A LEGEND OF KUPE

WHEN KUPE, the Polynesian explorer, came to Aotearoa more than a thousand years ago, he brought with him two birds. Rupe, the wood pigeon, was given the task of finding forest seeds and fruit. Te Kawau-a-toru was told to seek out all the tidal rivers and inlets. On arrival at the heads of the Manukau harbour, Te Kawau was sent out and came back with the report that the currents were not unduly strong.

Having proved its value, Kupe sent the bird to swim in all the rivers and harbours on the west coast of the North Island. In so doing the bird developed great strength in its wings and legs, and longed to find a current that would extend its powers to the full. Even the tidal rips of Raukawa, which men later called Cook Strait, were unable to daunt the shag.

While Kupe was sheltering at Worser Bay in Port Nicholson, Te Kawau met several birds that had come from the South Island.

"Do you know of any places where the currents of ocean or rivers of the land are strong?" Te Kawau asked. "I have conquered all the waters of this island."

"There are currents you'll never be able to overcome in our island," they replied proudly. "You must come and see them for yourself."

Te Kawau sought its master's permission, and promised to return and tell him what it had found. Kupe consented and settled for a while at Rimurapa, which the Pakeha knows as Sinclair Head, with his daughters.

When Te Kawau-a-toru, accompanied by the birds of the South Island, reached the narrow channel between Rangitoto (D'Urville Island) and the mainland, its attention was drawn to the water which swept through in an angry, swirling torrent.

"Ah! This is nothing to what you will see in a little while," the birds told Te Kawau. "Wait till the tide is full."

"That is the reason I came," said Te Kawau. "If I'm able to overcome the tide rips it will prove that they are weak and have no strength against my master's canoe."

They flew down and inspected the water closely.

"The current is flowing faster," they cried. "The time has come for you to try it. Your strength will never prevail against the torrents of Rangitoto."

Te Kawau swept down and touched the tidal rip with the tip of a wing, testing it as a bather might feel the water with his toes. The current was stronger than the bird thought. It caught its wing and held it so firmly that it was forced to its knees. Te Kawau advanced the other wing, but the birds cried out in shrill alarm, "O sir! You will be killed!"

Te Kawau was not frightened, even though one of its wings was stretched from one side of the channel to the other, held in the fierce grip of the water. It tried to raise itself by flapping the free wing, but in vain. Inexorably the flapping wing was forced down to the racing torrent. It surged round the gallant bird, swept it off its feet, and whirled it round like a chip of wood in

Te Kawau-a-toru at French Pass

the eddy of a stream. Te Kawau kept on struggling, but the wing was broken. The brave one of Kupe had at last met its match.

If Te Kawau-a-toru had won the struggle, the channel would have been tamed, and women could have paddled their canoes through in safety.

But the great-hearted bird was drowned. Fierce tides race through the perilous passage. It is known to the Pakeha as French Pass in honour of another brave one who met the challenge in a white-winged vessel.

The black-winged Kawau remains there for all time, petrified by an act of defiance into a boulder that still challenges the racing tides and rips of the pass that was named to commemorate the French navigator who broke its power a thousand years after Kupe left these enchanted islands.

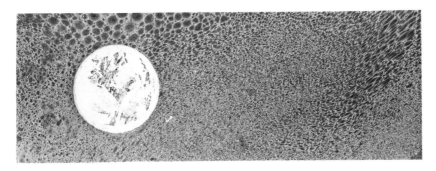

A LEGEND OF THE MOON

OF THE MANY LEGENDS of the heavenly bodies there is none more popular or widespread than the story of Rona, the woman in the moon.

She was loved by her husband but, as happens only too often, their lives were spoiled by her quick temper and the sharpness of her tongue.

There came a day when her husband said to her, "Tonight is one of the nights of the moon most favourable for fishing. I shall take the boys with me. We're going to the off-shore island where the fish are plentiful. We won't be back until tomorrow night. We should have a good catch by then. See that you have a good meal waiting for us."

The following day Rona prepared the oven and waited for her family to return home. When the shadows began to lengthen she lit the cooking fire. She had planned well, for as the heated stones glowed red in the dusk she heard the song of the returning fishermen. Before placing the food in the oven and covering it with greenery and earth, she discovered that she had no water to sprinkle over the hot stones.

The spring was at a little distance. Snatching up two calabashes she ran down the path. Darkness had fallen before she reached the spring, but a full moon was shining. The track showed up clearly in its silver light. Suddenly the moon was obscured by a passing cloud. Darkness rushed across the trees. She could not see her way and stubbed her toes on a projecting root. On trying to recover her balance she crashed into a rock and bruised her shin.

In her pain and exasperation she cursed the moon for having withdrawn its light.

"Pokokohua !" she shouted. "Cooked head!" — a malignant curse as well as an insulting epithet. The words were overheard by the moon, which descended from the sky and caught Rona in its hands and began to carry her away.

Rona caught at the branch of a ngaio tree and clung to it with all her might. But what use is it to fight against the gods? Although her grasp of the tree could not be broken, the roots were torn out of the ground and the woman was born aloft, far into the sky, and placed on the surface of the moon. There she remains for all to see. With her are her calabashes and the ngaio tree which remained in her grasp during the violent journey.

It was a sad home-coming for her husband and children. The fires of the umu still flickered. The uncooked food still lay beside the oven, but there was no sign of Rona.

It was not until they looked up at the night sky that they realised that their hot-tempered wife and mother had angered the gods, for on the face of the full-bodied moon they saw her sitting disconsolate with her calabashes and the uprooted ngaio tree.

"Kia mahara ki te he o Rona," says the old proverb.
Remember the wrongful act of Rona.

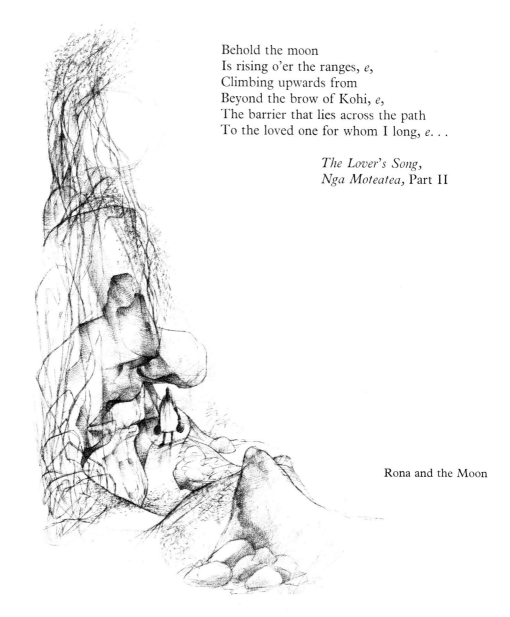

Behold the moon
Is rising o'er the ranges, *e,*
Climbing upwards from
Beyond the brow of Kohi, *e,*
The barrier that lies across the path
To the loved one for whom I long, *e. . .*

The Lover's Song,
Nga Moteatea, Part II

Rona and the Moon

THE RESTLESS MOUNTAINS

In the year 1864 Te Kani-a-takirau, the most powerful chief of the east coast, was proposed as Maori King. The offer was made by Te Heuheu of Taupo. Te Kani refused the invitation, saying that he was born a king and could not have kingship conferred on him.

Te Heuheu replied, "You may be king of the east coast, but I want you to be king of all the Maori people of Aotearoa and stamp out the mana of that woman queen."

"My kingdom is like my mountain Hikurangi," Te Kani said proudly. "It is inherited and permanent and not like your Tongariro, a wanderer."

The metaphor referred to the legend of the wandering mountains of the volcanic plateau, of which there are many versions.

In the long ago many mountains lived together in the centre of the North Island. Tongariro, not then truncated, but rearing his snow-clad form far into the clouds, was the ariki. Near him stood Taranaki (Mount Egmont), Tauhara and Putauaki. They were all proud and valiant warriors. The only woman among them was Pihanga, rounded in soft curves, clad in a cloak of green foliage.

The male mountains all coveted this gentle female mountain and fought fiercely for her love. Tongariro was the victor. He wrapped her in soft arms of cloud, and drove the other mountains far away. They departed at night and hastily, for they knew that their progress would be arrested by the rising sun.

Tauhara and Putauaki journeyed towards the sea. Tauhara was the tardy one, often looking backwards, and progressed no further than the northern shore of Lake Taupo. Putauaki travelled to the end of the Kaingaroa Plain and, as Mount Edgecumbe, stands as the sentinel of the Bay of Plenty.

Taranaki, mightier than Tauhara and Putauaki, said, "Ka haere au ki te towenetanga o te ra" — "I shall go to the setting place of the sun." He ploughed a mighty furrow, down which the Wanganui river flows, and took up a position on the western tip of the island, where he still hurls taunts at the victorious Tongariro.

TOHUNGA AND MAKUTU

THERE WERE several grades of tohunga, the priests and experts of Maori society. The highest were the tohunga ahurewa, the lowest the tohunga kehua. Among them were many specialists, such as the tohunga tatai-arorangi who interpreted the passage and appearance of the stars, the tohunga makutu who used the power of black magic to kill, the tohunga matakite who foretold future events. Not infrequently the powers of rival tohunga were put to the test, and a conflict developed to prove which was the one most thoroughly versed in the arts of the whare-maire. Such is the story of Hakawau and Paawa.

Both the tohunga had fallen in love with Rona, a kiritea of charm and beauty. Hakawau lived far away at Kawhia and had never declared his love— nor had Paawa, an evil tohunga who had power over many atua. Seizing an opportunity when the girl was not closely guarded, the tohunga snatched her away from her home and imprisoned her in his own pa.

As soon as he learnt of Rona's abduction her brother Korokia hastily assembled a war party and set out to rescue her. The men were afraid of Paawa's unearthly powers and crept through the bush, avoiding the forest trails. They hoped to take the tohunga's pa by surprise. On reaching the edge of the forest they closed their ranks and ran across the open space in front of the pa, but before they could reach it some madness seized them. Many fell lifeless to the ground, others turned on their friends and fierce fighting broke out among them. Of the one hundred and forty men who set out on the war path only one escaped. Korokia was the sole survivor of the gallant band.

He returned sadly to his home and sent a message to Hakawau, who was noted for his prowess in battle, to lead another taua against Paawa. The young chief was anxious to help his friend and to rescue the girl for whom he had a secret affection, but he knew that he was no match for Paawa.

"You must be patient," he said to Korokia. "I will go to the warlocks of the Urewera and learn the secrets of their black art. Then and only then can we hope to subdue Paawa."

It was many months before he returned from his arduous course of makutu. He went directly to Korokia's pa and said, "I have learnt the karakia that will overcome Paawa's evil, the magic that will grind his face in the dust."

It was a small force that followed Hakawau and Korokia, for few ablebodied men were left in the village. They made no attempt to hide themselves from the enemy and soon arrived in sight of Paawa's fortress. Hakawau went forward slowly. His warriors saw Paawa standing alone on the watch tower, but Hakawau's trained eyes could also see a host of evil atua trooping out of the gate and converging on his men. Summoning all his strength and drawing on the knowledge he had learnt from the experts of Tuhoe in the gloomy Urewera forests, he chanted the karakia that would summon their atua to his aid.

On the field of battle there were only two men who could see the ghostly warriors closing in to the attack. The cries of contending spirits, the thud of weapons, the hoarse panting of the fighters, and the moans of the wounded rang in the ears of Hakawau and Paawa. For a time the issue was in doubt but at last the atua of Urewera routed the spirits that Paawa had summoned to his aid.

Hakawau returned to his men. "Let us go forward," he said. "The time of vengeance has come."

One of the boldest warriors, whom none could accuse of cowardice, caught his arm. "O Hakawau!" he said, "I know that you are fearless but I tremble at your command. I can fight with flesh and blood, but the ghostly wairua will kill us before we can reach the outer palisades of the pa."

Hakawau looked at him in surprise.

"The fighting is over," he said. "I have been watching it. The atua of Paawa are dead. See for yourself."

He led the way, his men following reluctantly. They had seen nothing of the conflict, but they trusted their leader. He led them through the unmanned mazes of the palisades. Paawa was no longer standing on the watch tower. He had seen the defeat of his atua. His mana had been taken from him. He stood with bowed head.

Hakawau strode up to him. "Your power has gone, Paawa," he said sternly. "Your karakia availed little against mine. I will not kill you. I have shamed you this day. Remember in humility that your life was spared by Hakawau. You are no longer a tohunga, nor a rangatira. You are now a tutua, a person of mean birth.

"And now, where is Rona?" he demanded abruptly.

The discredited tohunga meekly led his opponent to a whare and slid back the door. Rona came out. She was indeed a kiritea, whom all men might desire. Her skin was fair, her limbs were rounded, she was graceful in all her movements—and in her eyes was a soft light of love for the young tohunga of Kawhia.

The Atua of Hakawau and Paawa

GLOSSARY

Ao-marama: World of life and light.

Aotearoa: New Zealand (Long White Cloud, Long Bright Land, Land of Long-lingering Daylight, etc.)

Ariki: Leader; first-born in notable family; priest.

Atua: God; demon; supernatural being.

Hangi: Oven of hot stones in the earth.

Haumia-tiketike: God who presided over fernroot.

Hawaiki: The homeland of the Maori race.

Hihi: Stitch-bird, *Notiomystis cincta.*

Hine-nui-o-te-po: Goddess of death.

Huhu: Larva of the beetle *Prionoplus reticularis,* found in rotting timber.

Kainga: viilage (unfortified).

Kaka: Green parrot, *Nestor meridionalis.*

Karakia: Incantation.

Kauri: Tree, *Agathis australis.*

Kawau: Shag—various species.

Kiritea: Fair.

Kiwi: Wingless nocturnal bird, *Apterix* of various species.

Kohukohu: Moss.

Kokako: Blue-wattled crow, *Callaeas cinerea wilsoni;* orange-wattled crow, *C. cinerea cinerea.*

Kokiri: Spear.

Kokowai: Red ochre.

Kore: Nothing.

Kumara: Sweet potato, *Ipomoea batatas.*

Kura: Red ochre.

Maero: Fabulous monster.

Maipi: Wooden weapon.

Makutu: Bewitch; magic; spell.

Mana: Prestige; influence.

Manuka: Tea-tree, *Leptospermum scoparium* and *L. ericoides.*

Maunganui: Great Mountain.

Mere: Short flat weapon of stone or greenstone.

Moa: Extinct giant flightless bird, *Dinornis gigantis* and other species.

Moko: General term for lizards.

Mokopuna: Grandchild; descendant.

Ngaio: Tree, *Myoporum laetum.*

Pa: Fortified place.

Patupaiarehe: Fairy.

Po: Night.

Pohutukawa: Tree, *Metrosideros excelsa.*

Pokokohua: Epithet considered an unforgivable curse. (From *Upoko,* head, and *Kohua,* to cook by boiling with heated stones.)

Ponaturi: Mythical beings who sleep on land, but retire under the sea during daytime.

Poua-kai: Fabulous giant bird.

Pounamu: Greenstone.

Puku: Abdomen.

Rangatira: Chief; noble.

Rarohenga: The underworld.

Raupo: Reed, *Typha muelleri.*

Reinga: Place of departing spirits, "The place of leaping", where the spirits took their final plunge to the underworld.

Rupe: Pigeon, *Hemiphaga novaeseelandiae.*

Taiaha: Hardwood weapon about five feet long with pointed tongue and narrow blade.

Tamariki: Children.

Taniwha: Fabulous monster residing in deep water.

Tapu: Sacred; forbidden; inaccessible; not to be defiled.

Tataramoa: Bramble, *Rubus cissoides.*

Taua: War party.

Tawhiri-matea: God of Winds.

Te Kawau-a-toru: See *Kawau.*

Te Kore: The Nothing.

Te Po: The Night.

Te Ra: The Sun.

Tewhatewha: Weapon shaped like an axe, carved in one piece.

Ti: Cabbage tree, *Cordyline* of several species.

Tieke: Saddleback, *Philesturnus carunculatus.*

Tipua: Goblin.

Tohunga: Priest; wizard; skilled person.

Toutouwai: North Island robin, *Miro longipes;* South Island robin, *M. australis.*

Tuatete: A reptile like a large lizard.

Tu-matauenga: God of war.

Tutua: Person of low degree.

Umu: Earth oven.

Uru: Ancient western land of Maori legend; brother of Tane-mahuta.

Wairua: Spirit.

Waka taua: War canoe.

Whare: House.

Whaka (Whanga in the North Island): Bay; harbour; hollow.

Whare-maire: House where sacred lore was taught.

Whare-puni: Sleeping-house.

Whare tapere: House of amusement.